CW00351404

JUST BEARS

Martin Leman's
JUST BEARS

PELHAM BOOKS

POOH'S *Hum*

Breathlessly
I lay on my chest
And I thought it best
To pretend I was having an evening rest;
I lay on my tum
And I tried to hum
But nothing particular seemed to come.

My face was flat
On the floor, and that
Is all very well for an acrobat;
But it doesn't seem fair
To a Friendly Bear
To stiffen him out with a basket-chair.

And a sort of sqoze
Which grows and grows
Is not too nice for his poor old nose,
And a sort of squch
Is much too much
For his neck and his mouth and his ears and such.

AA Milne

BEAR *Facts*

There are a great many species of bear,
and none of them wear underwear,
and most of them like to climb tall trees,
but very seldom graze their knees!

Bob Devereux

Isabel's
ADVENTURE

Isabel met an enormous bear,
Isabel, Isabel, didn't care.
The bear was hungry, the bear was ravenous,
The bear's big mouth was cruel and cavernous.
The bear said, Isabel, glad to meet you,
How do, Isabel, now I'll eat you!
Isabel, Isabel, didn't worry;
Isabel didn't scream or scurry.
She washed her hands and she straightened her hair up,
Then Isabel quietly ate the bear up...

Ogden Nash

The Boss-eyed BEAR

The Boss-eyed bear
Got his eyes crossed badly,
When Aunty sewed them on.
And sadly, nobody has ever, quite,
Repaired the poor bear's bad eye sight.

Bob Devereux

Special BEARS

Old bears, young bears, baggy bears and tight ones,
Big bears, little bears, brown bears and white ones,
Fat bears, thin bears, nosy bears, polite ones,
Funny bears, sad bears, morning bears and night ones,
Every bear's a special bear – no wrong'uns only right'uns.

Jill Leman

Fore BEARS

This Bear
Forbears
To mention
His forebears
Who were
Four bears
Of noble birth
A bear who brags
Is more than he can bear

Bob Devereux

Teddy BEAR

Your furry body,
So velvety when I touch it,
Your brown beady eyes,
Stare at me.
When I am sad,
You are a shoulder to cry on.
My dear teddy bear.

Nana Taylor

STOCK *Exchange*

There's a Bull and a Bear, and what do you think?
They live in a Garden of white Stocks and pink.
'I'll give you a pink Stock for one of your white,'
Says the Bear to the Bull, and the Bull says, 'All right!'
They never make answer if anyone knocks,
They are always so busy exchanging their Stocks.

Eleanor Farjeon

SING *Ho!*

With plenty of spirit

Sing Ho! for the life of a Bear!
Sing Ho! for the life a Bear!
I don't much mind if it rains or snows,
'Cos I've got a lot of honey on my nice new nose!
I don't much care if it snows or thaws,
'Cos I've got a lot of honey on my nice clean paws!
Sing Ho! for the life of a Bear!
Sing Ho! for a Pooh!
And I'll have a little something in an hour or two!
Sing Ho! for a Bear!
Sing Ho! for a Pooh!
And I'll have a little something in an hour or two!

AA Milne

Fuzzy BEAR

Fuzzy is my favourite bear,
I really care about him,
I take him out,
I feed him.
He has chestnut beady eyes,
And a white furry silky coat.
Where I go he goes, and that's the end of that.

Anouska Hartley

NED'S *Story*

If bears like these had memories
what stories they would tell,
of crumpets round the nursery fire
and picnics by the well,
of getting lost in Windy Wood,
and being found by Ned,
and wrapped up in a tartan shawl,
and taken home to bed.

Such bears as these had luxuries
most bears will never see.
A butler and a chambermaid,
a cook and a nanny.
All came to say hello to them,
when they came down to tea,
And Dukes and Duchesses were told
just how they had survived,
three nights out in the Windy Woods,
where owls and foxes lived.

Ned's mother said, 'They have been brave.'
Ned's father said, 'Good, good!'

Bob Devereux

Teddy BEARS

I never had a teddy bear
All those years ago,
A bear I could rely on,
To tell my troubles to.
A bear who liked affection
and never shook a head,
A bear to hug and cuddle,
and take with me to bed.

Martin Leman

Bathtub BEAR

Bear in a cupboard
Bear up a tree
Bear in a bathtub
Bare as can be

Bob Devereux

 The FRIEND

There are lots and lots of people who are always
   asking things,
Like Dates and Pounds-and-ounces and the names of
   funny Kings,
And the answer's either Sixpence or A Hundred
   Inches Long.
And I know they'll think me silly if I get the answer
   wrong.

So Pooh and I go whispering, and Pooh looks very
   bright,
And says, 'Well, I say sixpence, but I don't suppose I'm
   right.'
And then it doesn't matter what the answer ought
   to be,
Cos if he's right, I'm Right, and if he's wrong,
   it isn't Me.

AA Milne

Bazaar BEAR

It's very rare to find a bear at a church bazaar.

Nothing is more bizarre than an abandoned bear,
discovered in a corner on a chair,
next to a row of overcoats which smell of mothballs
and a pile of old rags nobody would wear.

But, if I should chance to find him first,
you wouldn't find him there.

Bob Devereux

Infant INNOCENCE

The Grizzly Bear is huge and wild;
He has devoured the infant child.
The infant child is not aware
He has been eaten by the bear.

AE Housman

Funny BEARS

The thing I've found,
Is it a bear?
He's tattered and brown,
His big ears stick out,
His fur is worn down,
He's chubby.
He falls from the cupboard
The stuffing falls down to his feet!
He's cuddly and funny
He is a bear!
He's going to be my friend.

Louise McIntyre

Bruin's RUIN

There was an old bear named Bruin,
who went on a day trip to Turin.
He went to a fair
and they made him dance there
and dancing was poor Bruin's ruin.

Bob Devereux

Martin Leman would like to thank everyone
who lent their teddy bears for the photographs
in this book, and special thanks to
Sarah Watson of St Ives, Cornwall.

The authors and publisher would like to thank the following
for permission to use poems:
A.A. Milne, Methuen Children's Books and E.P. Dutton for
poems from *The Hums of Pooh* and *Now We Are Six*.
Ogden Nash, Little, Brown and Company and Curtis Brown for
'The Adventures of Isabel' from *Custard and Company*.
Eleanor Farjeon and Duckworth for 'The Stock Exchange' from
Nursery Rhymes of London Town.
The Society of Authors as literary executors of AE Housman's
estate and Jonathan Cape for 'Infant Innocence'.
Jane Moyes, Louise McIntyre, Nana Taylor and Anouska Hartley
of Highfield School, London.
Bob Devereux of St Ives, Cornwall.

PELHAM BOOKS

Published by the Penguin Group,
27 Wrights Lane, London W8 5TZ, England
Viking Penguin., 375 Hudson Street, New York, New York 10014, USA
Penguin Books Australia Ltd, Ringwood, Victoria, Australia
Penguin Books Canada Ltd, 10 Alcorn Avenue, Toronto, Ontario, Canada M4V 3B2
Penguin Books (NZ) Ltd, 182-190 Wairau Road, Auckland 10, New Zealand

Penguin Books Ltd, Registered Offices: Harmondsworth, Middlesex, England

First published 1992
Reprinted 1992

Copyright © Jill and Martin Leman 1992

All rights reserved. Without limiting the rights under copyright reserved
above, no part of this publication may be reproduced, stored
in or introduced into a retrieval system, or transmitted, in any form
or by any means (electronic, mechanical, photocopying, recording or
otherwise), without the prior written permission of both the
copyright owner and the above publisher of this book.

Research and design by Jill Leman

Typeset by Panache, London
Colour origination by Anglia Graphics, Bedford
Printed and bound by William Clowes Ltd, Beccles and London

A CIP catalogue record for this book is available from the British Library

ISBN 0 7207 2017 6

The moral right of the authors has been asserted